ALTO SAX
Showstoppers

D1287669

© 1993 CPP/Belwin, Inc.
15800 N.W. 48th Avenue, Miami, Florida 33014

Design: Jeannette Aquino, Frank Milone
Production Coordinators: Carol Cuellar, David C. Olsen

CONTENTS

AFTER ALL (Love Theme From "Chances Are") 16
AGAINST ALL ODDS (Take A Look At Me Now) 4
ALFIE 5
ALWAYS 6
ALWAYS AND FOREVER 8
ANYTHING FOR YOU 10
AXEL F 11
BABY, COME TO ME 12
BABY ELEPHANT WALK 13
CALIFORNIA GIRLS 14
CLASSICAL GAS 15
COLOUR MY WORLD 17
COMING AROUND AGAIN 18
DO YOU LOVE ME 19
DO YOU WANT TO KNOW A SECRET? 20
(Sittin' On) THE DOCK OF THE BAY 21
DON'T CRY OUT LOUD 22
DON'T FALL IN LOVE WITH A DREAMER 23
DON'T IT MAKE MY BROWN EYES BLUE 24
DON'T WANNA LOSE YOU 71
ENTERTAINMENT TONIGHT 26
FALLING IN LOVE (Uh Oh) 27
FAME 28
FOOTLOOSE 30
FOR ONCE IN MY LIFE 29
FOR YOUR EYES ONLY 32
FOREVER'S AS FAR AS I'LL GO 7
FROM A DISTANCE 33
GEORGIA ON MY MIND 49
GHOSTBUSTERS 34
GIVING YOU THE BEST THAT I GOT 35
GONNA FLY NOW (Theme from "Rocky") 36
THE GREATEST LOVE OF ALL 37
HARD TO SAY I'M SORRY 38
THE HEAT IS ON 40
HERE WE ARE 60
HEY, GOOD LOOKIN' 41
HEY! BABY! 42
THE HOUSE OF THE RISING SUN 44
HOW WILL I KNOW 45
HUNGRY EYES (from "Dirty Dancing") 46
(Everything I Do) I DO IT FOR YOU 43
I DON'T HAVE THE HEART 92
I JUST CALLED TO SAY I LOVE YOU 47
('Til) I KISSED YOU 48

IF EVER YOU'RE IN MY ARMS AGAIN 50
ISN'T SHE LOVELY 51
IT MIGHT BE YOU (Theme From "Tootsie") 52
I'LL NEVER LOVE THIS WAY AGAIN 54
JUST THE TWO OF US 55
THE LADY IN RED 56

LAST DATE (Instrumental) 57
LINUS AND LUCY 58
LOVE THEME FROM "ST. ELMO'S FIRE" 59
MOON RIVER 61
MORE THAN WORDS 63
MY LOVE 62
NOBODY LOVES ME LIKE YOU DO 64
OH, PRETTY WOMAN 65
OLD TIME ROCK AND ROLL 111
ON GREEN DOLPHIN STREET 66
ON THE WINGS OF LOVE 67
ONE IN A MILLION YOU 68
OVER THE RAINBOW 69
THE PINK PANTHER 70
PUT A LITTLE LOVE IN YOUR HEART 25
READY TO TAKE A CHANCE AGAIN 72
RISE 74
(Love Theme from) ROMEO AND JULIET 75
SEPARATE LIVES (Love Theme from "White Nights") 76
SIGNS 73
SINGING THE BLUES 77
SIR DUKE 78
STAR DUST 79
STILL 80
ST. ELMO'S FIRE (Man In Motion) 81
SWEET LOVE 83
TAKE MY BREATH AWAY (Love Theme from "Top Gun") 84
THEME FROM ICE CASTLES (Through The Eyes Of Love) 85
THEME FROM NEW YORK, NEW YORK 86
THEME FROM "CHEERS" (Where Everybody Knows Your Name)...... 88
THEME FROM "TERMS OF ENDEARMENT" 90
THIS OLD HEART OF MINE (Is Weak For You) 98
(I've Had) THE TIME OF MY LIFE 87
TO ME 93
TOMORROW 95
TONIGHT, I CELEBRATE MY LOVE 96
TRAVELIN' MAN 97
UP WHERE WE BELONG 99
THE WAY HE MAKES ME FEEL 100
THE WAY YOU DO THE THINGS YOU DO 82
WE'VE ONLY JUST BEGUN 101
WHAT'S GOING ON 102
WHAT'S LOVE GOT TO DO WITH IT 103
A WHITE SPORT COAT (And A Pink Carnation) 104
YOU AND I 106
YOU ARE THE SUNSHINE OF MY LIFE 105
YOU GOT IT ALL 108
YOU GOTTA LOVE SOMEONE 94
YOU LIGHT UP MY LIFE 109
YOU'RE THE INSPIRATION 110

COLUMBIA PICTURES Presents RACHEL WARD, JEFF BRIDGES and JAMES WOODS In
"AGAINST ALL ODDS"

AGAINST ALL ODDS
(Take A Look At Me Now)

By PHIL COLLINS

From the Paramount Picture "ALFIE"

ALFIE

Lyric by HAL DAVID

Music by BURT BACHARACH

ALWAYS

Written by
JONATHAN LEWIS, DAVID LEWIS
and WAYNE LEWIS

Moderately slow

FOREVER'S AS FAR AS I'LL GO

Slowly ♩ = 69

By MIKE REID

ALWAYS AND FOREVER

Words and Music by
ROD TEMPERTON

Always And Forever - 2 - 1

ANYTHING FOR YOU

Words and Music by
GLORIA M. ESTEFAN

AXEL F

By HAROLD FALTERMEYER

Moderately Bright

BABY, COME TO ME

By ROD TEMPERTON

From the Paramount Picture "HATARI"

BABY ELEPHANT WALK

By HENRY MANCINI

Moderately Slow and steady

CALIFORNIA GIRLS

By BRIAN WILSON

Moderate shuffle

mf

CLASSICAL GAS

By MASON WILLIAMS

From The Tri-Star Pictures film "CHANCES ARE"

AFTER ALL
(Love Theme From "Chances Are")

By
DEAN PITCHFORD and
TOM SNOW

From The "BALLET FOR A GIRL IN BUCHANNON" From The Columbia L.P. "CHICAGO"®

COLOUR MY WORLD

By JAMES PANKOW

(From The Paramount Motion Picture "Heartburn")

COMING AROUND AGAIN

By CARLY SIMON

DO YOU LOVE ME

Words and Music by
BERRY GORDY

Moderately up ♩=126

DO YOU WANT TO KNOW A SECRET?

By
JOHN LENNON and
PAUL McCARTNEY

(Sittin' On)
THE DOCK OF THE BAY

By
STEVE CROPPER and
OTIS REDDING

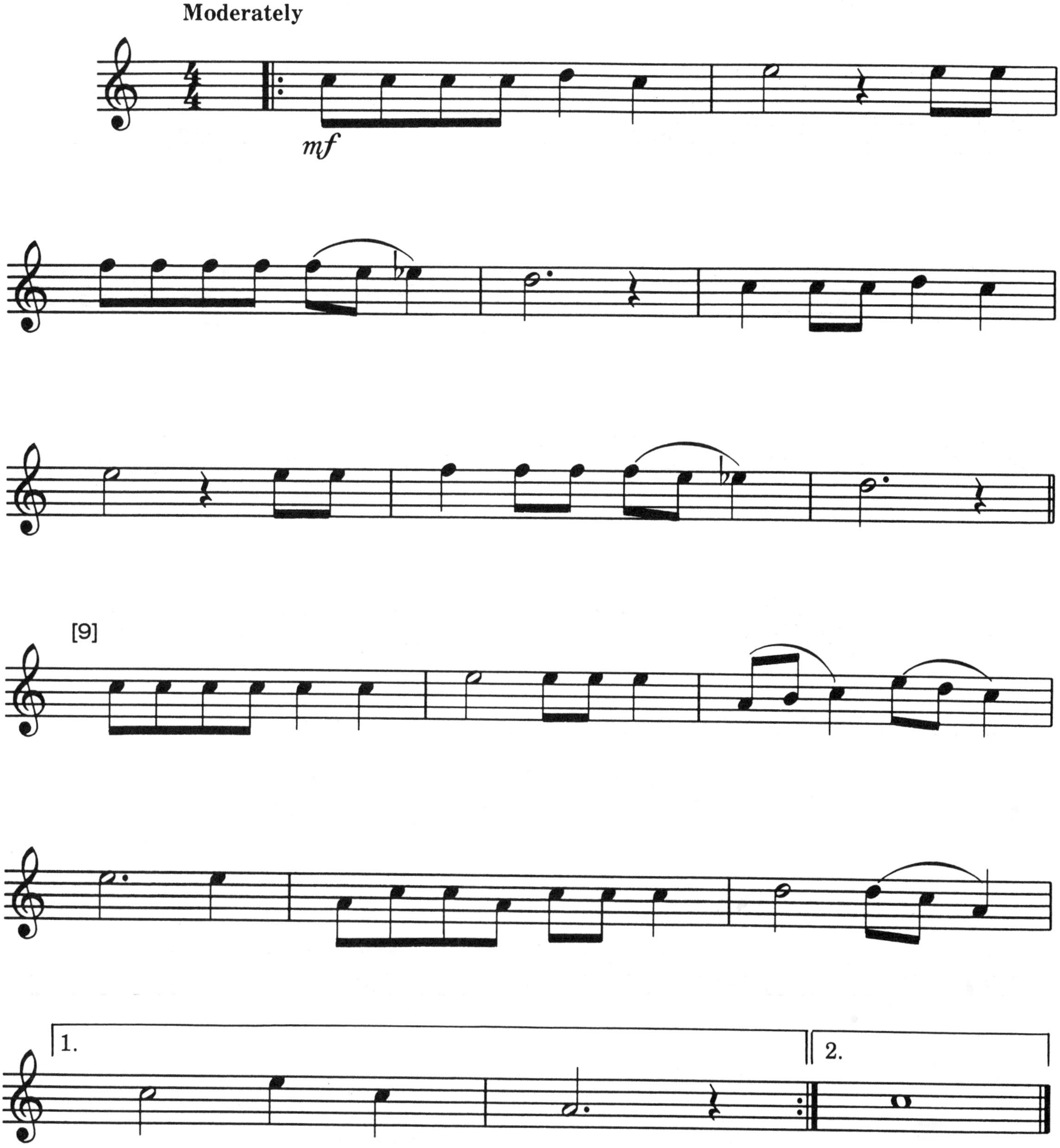

DON'T CRY OUT LOUD

By
PETER ALLEN and
CAROLE BAYER SAGER

DON'T FALL IN LOVE WITH A DREAMER

By
KIM CARNES and
DAVE ELLINGSON

Slowly

rit. e dim.

DON'T IT MAKE MY BROWN EYES BLUE

By RICHARD LEIGH

From The Paramount Motion Picture "SCROOGED"

PUT A LITTLE LOVE IN YOUR HEART

Words and Music by
JIMMY HOLIDAY, RANDY MYERS
and JACKIE DE SHANNON

From Paramount Television and Video Distribution

ENTERTAINMENT TONIGHT

Music by
MICHAEL MARK

Moderately Fast

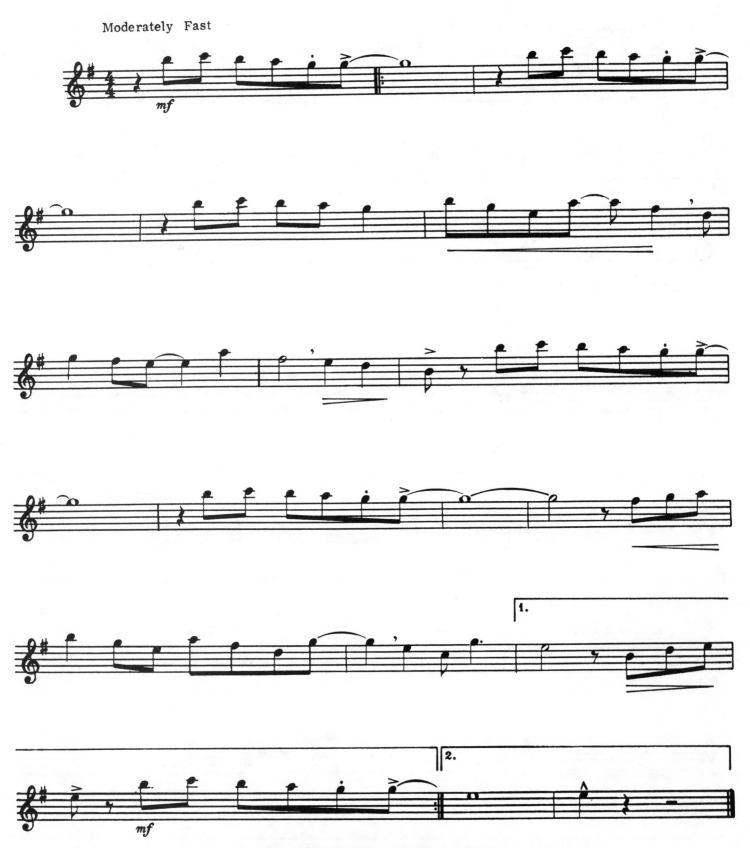

FALLING IN LOVE
(Uh-Oh)

By
LAWRENCE DERMER, JOE GALDO
and RAFAEL VIGIL

Moderately

FAME

By
DEAN PITCHFORD and
MICHAEL GORE

FOR ONCE IN MY LIFE

Lyric by RONALD MILLER

Music by ORLANDO MURDEN

to Coda

D.S. al Coda

Coda

Paramount Pictures Presents A Daniel Melnick Production A Herbert Ross Film "FOOTLOOSE"

FOOTLOOSE

Written by
KENNY LOGGINS and
DEAN PITCHFORD

Fast rock and roll

Footloose - 2 - 1

Footloose - 2 - 2

FOR YOUR EYES ONLY

Lyrics by MICHAEL LEESON
Music by BILL CONTI

Moderately Slow

rit. e dim.

FROM A DISTANCE

Lyrics and Music by
JULIE GOLD

COLUMBIA PICTURES Presents An IVAN REITMAN Film
A BLACK RHINO/BERNIE BRILLSTEIN Production "GHOSTBUSTERS"

GHOSTBUSTERS

Words and Music by
RAY PARKER, JR.

Moderately bright rock

GIVING YOU THE BEST THAT I GOT

Words and Music by
ANITA BAKER, SKIP SCARBOROUGH
and RANDY HOLLAND

From the UNITED ARTISTS Motion Picture "ROCKY"

GONNA FLY NOW
(Theme From "ROCKY")

By
BILL CONTI, AYN ROBBINS
and CAROL CONNORS

Briskly

(From the Columbia Motion Picture "THE GREATEST") A Columbia/EMI Presentation

THE GREATEST LOVE OF ALL

Words by LINDA CREED

Music by MICHAEL MASSER

Slowly

HARD TO SAY I'M SORRY

By
PETER CETERA and
DAVID FOSTER

Moderately Slow

Hard To Say I'm Sorry - 2 - 1

D.S. al Coda

Coda

Hard To Say I'm Sorry - 2 - 2

rit.

f

From The Paramount Motion Picture "BEVERLY HILLS COP"

THE HEAT IS ON

Music by HAROLD FALTERMEYER
Words by KEITH FORSEY

HEY, GOOD LOOKIN'

By HANK WILLIAMS

HEY! BABY!

Words and Music by
MARGARET COBB and
BRUCE CHANNEL

D.C. al Fine

(EVERYTHING I DO) I DO IT FOR YOU

By
BRYAN ADAMS, R.J. LANGE
and M. KAMEN

Slowly ♩ = 66

THE HOUSE OF THE RISING SUN

By
ALAN PRICE

HOW WILL I KNOW

Words and Music by
GEORGE MERRILL, SHANNON RUBICAM
and NARADA MICHAEL WALDEN

Moderately

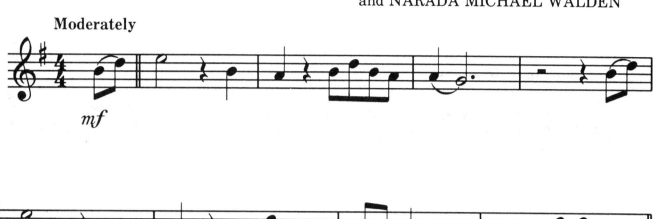

From The Vestron Motion Picture "Dirty Dancing"

HUNGRY EYES

Words and Music by
FRANKE PREVITE and
JOHN DeNICOLA

I JUST CALLED TO SAY I LOVE YOU

Words and Music by
STEVIE WONDER

('Til) I KISSED YOU

Words and Music by
DON EVERLY

GEORGIA ON MY MIND

Lyrics by
STUART GORRELL

Music by
HOAGY CARMICHAEL

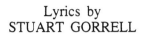

IF EVER YOU'RE IN MY ARMS AGAIN

Words and Music by
MICHAEL MASSER, TOM SNOW
and CYNTHIA WEIL

Moderately Slow

ISN'T SHE LOVELY

By STEVIE WONDER

Moderately Fast

COLUMBIA PICTURES Presents a MIRAGE/PUNCH Production a Sidney Pollack Film "TOOTSIE"

IT MIGHT BE YOU
(Theme From Tootsie)

Words by
ALAN and MARILYN BERGMAN
Music by DAVE GRUSIN

Slowly, with expression

It Might Be You 2 1

D.S. al Coda

Coda

It Might Be You - 2 - 2

rit. e dim.

I'LL NEVER LOVE THIS WAY AGAIN

Words by WILL JENNINGS
Music by RICHARD KERR

JUST THE TWO OF US

By
RALPH MacDONALD, WILLIAM SALTER
and BILL WITHERS

THE LADY IN RED

Words and Music by
CHRIS DeBURGH

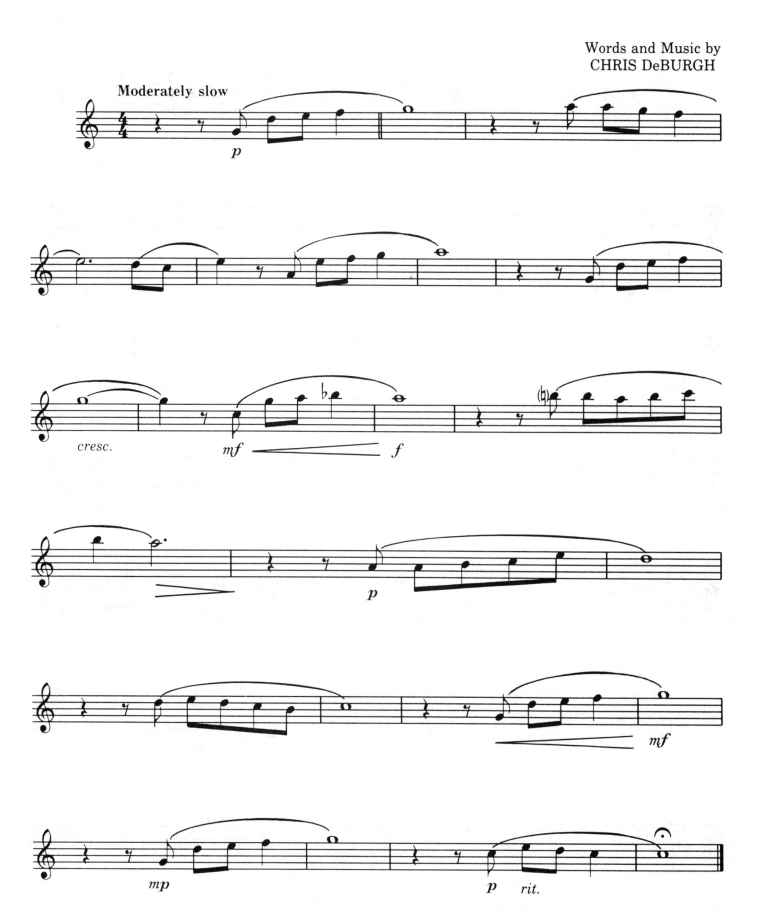

LAST DATE
(Instrumental)

By FLOYD CRAMER

LINUS & LUCY

By
VINCE GUARALDI

Columbia Pictures Presents A Channel-Lauren Shuler Production
A Joel Schumacher Film "ST. ELMO'S FIRE"

LOVE THEME FROM "ST. ELMO'S FIRE"

(Instrumental)

By
DAVID FOSTER

HERE WE ARE

Words and Music by
GLORIA ESTEFAN

Slowly ♩ = 72

F3075ASX

As Sung in the Paramount Picture "BREAKFAST AT TIFFANY'S"

MOON RIVER

Words by JOHNNY MERCER

Music by HENRY MANCINI

MY LOVE

Words and Music by
STEVIE WONDER

MORE THAN WORDS

By
BETTENCOURT, CHERONE

Moderately slow ♩ = 92

F3188ASX

NOBODY LOVES ME LIKE YOU DO

Words by
PAMELA PHILLIPS

Music by
JAMES P. DUNNE

OH, PRETTY WOMAN

By ROY ORBISON and BILL DEES

Medium rock

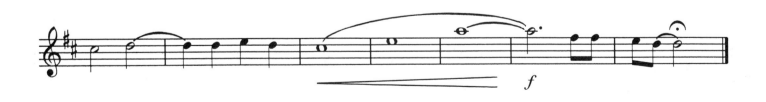

ON GREEN DOLPHIN STREET

Words by NED WASHINGTON
Music by BRONISLAU KAPER

ON THE WINGS OF LOVE

Words by JEFFREY OSBORNE
Music by PETER SCHLESS

Moderately Slow

ONE IN A MILLION YOU

By SAM DEES

From The Metro-Goldwyn-Mayer Musical Production "THE WIZARD OF OZ"

OVER THE RAINBOW

Words by E.Y. HARBURG
Music by HAROLD ARLEN

Theme Song From The Mirisch-G&E Production, THE PINK PANTHER, A United Artists Release

THE PINK PANTHER

By HENRY MANCINI

Moderato Misterioso

DON'T WANNA LOSE YOU

By GLORIA ESTEFAN

Moderately slow ♩ = 80

From the Paramount Picture "FOUL PLAY"

READY TO TAKE A CHANCE AGAIN

Words by NORMAN GIMBEL

Music by CHARLES FOX

SIGNS

By
LES EMMERSON

RISE

By
ANDY ARMER and
RANDY BADAZZ

From The Paramount Picture "ROMEO AND JULIET"

(Love Theme From)
ROMEO AND JULIET

By NINO ROTA

Slowly and very expressively

Columbia Pictures Presents A New Vision Production "WHITE NIGHTS"

SEPARATE LIVES
(Love Theme From "WHITE NIGHTS")

By
STEPHEN BISHOP

SINGING THE BLUES

By MELVIN ENDSLEY

SIR DUKE

By
STEVIE WONDER

STARDUST

Words by MITCHELL PARISH
Music by HOAGY CARMICHAEL

STILL

By LIONEL B. RICHIE, JR.

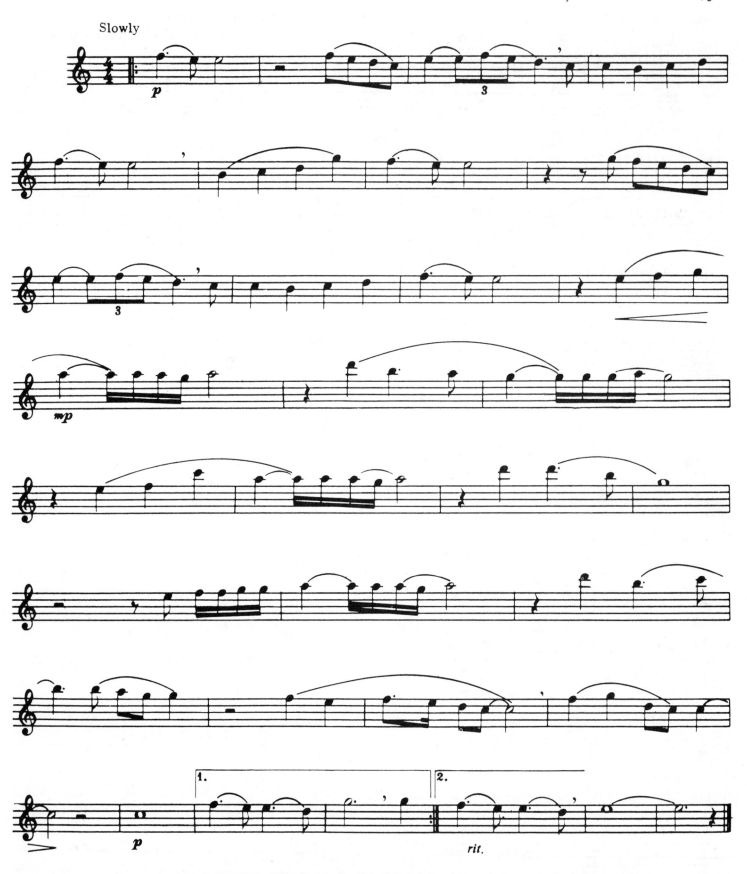

Columbia Pictures Presents A Channel-Lauren Shuler Production
A Joel Schumacher Film "ST. ELMO'S FIRE"

ST. ELMO'S FIRE

(MAN IN MOTION)

By
JOHN PARR and
DAVID FOSTER

Moderate Rock

THE WAY YOU DO THE THINGS YOU DO

By
WILLIAM "SMOKEY" ROBINSON"
and BOBBY ROGERS

Reggae ♩ = 80

SWEET LOVE

By
ANITA BAKER, LOUIS A. JOHNSON
& GARY BIAS

TAKE MY BREATH AWAY
(Love Theme From "Top Gun")

By
GIORGIO MORODER &
TOM WHITLOCK

From the Columbia Picture "ICE CASTLES"

THEME FROM ICE CASTLES
(Through The Eyes Of Love)

Lyrics by CAROLE BAYER SAGER
Music by MARVIN HAMLISCH

From The United Artists Motion Picture "NEW YORK, NEW YORK"

THEME FROM NEW YORK, NEW YORK

Words by FRED EBB
Music by JOHN KANDER

Moderately, with rhythm

from the Vestron Motion Picture "Dirty Dancing"

(I'VE HAD) THE TIME OF MY LIFE

Words and Music by
FRANKE PREVITE, DONALD MARKOWITZ
and JOHN DeNICOLA

From Charles/Burrows/Charles Productions In Association With Paramount Television

THEME FROM "CHEERS"
(Where Everybody Knows Your Name)

By
GARY PORTNOY and
JUDY HART ANGELO

Theme From "Cheers" - 2 - 1

Theme From "Cheers" - 2 - 2

THEME FROM "TERMS OF ENDEARMENT"

By MICHAEL GORE

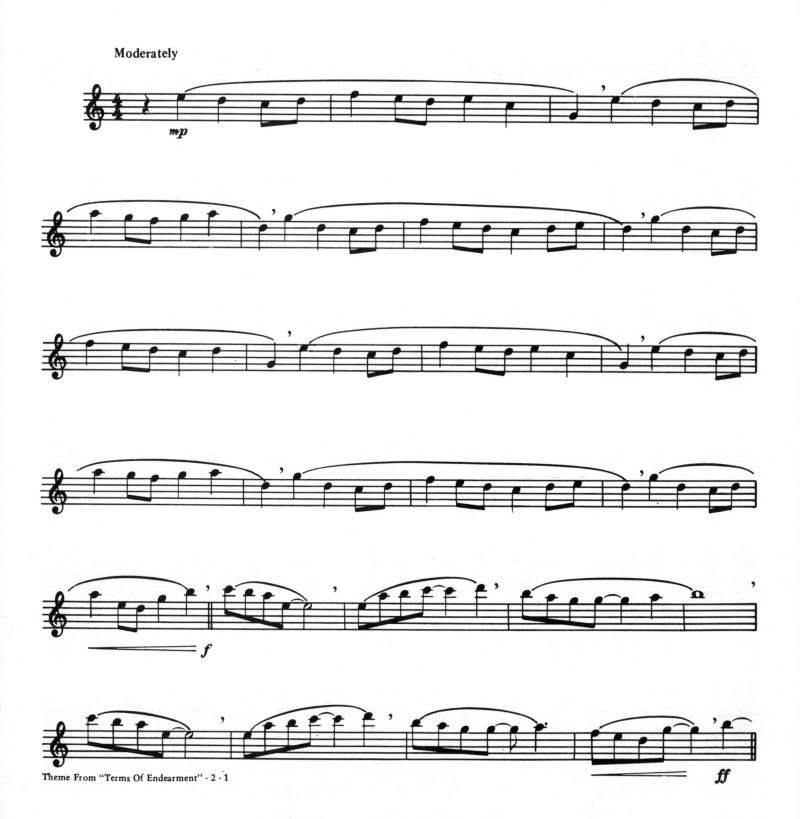

Theme From "Terms Of Endearment" - 2 - 1

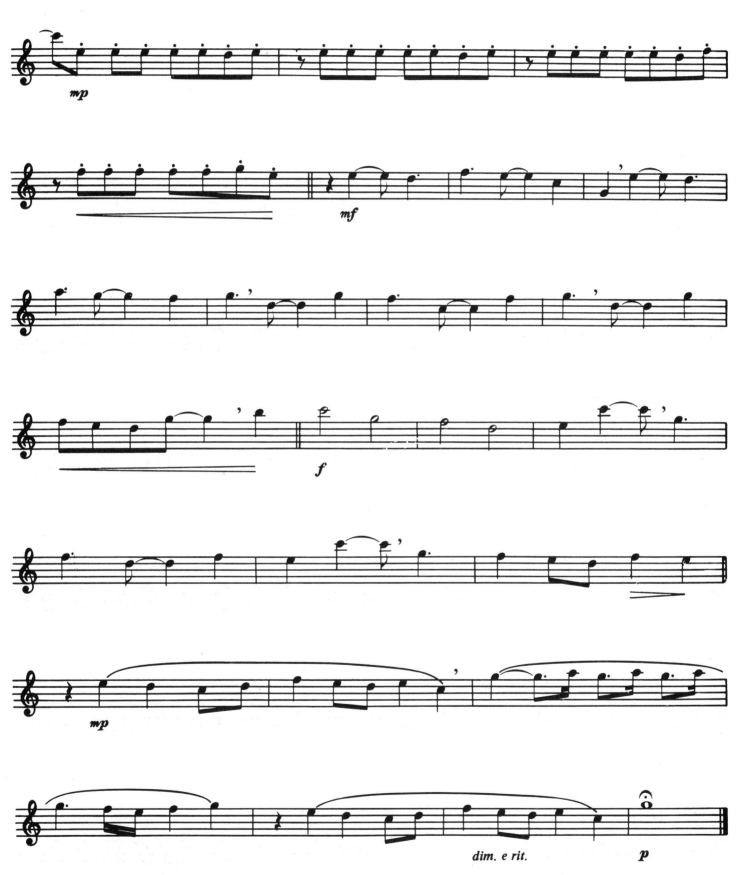

Theme From "Terms Of Endearment" - 2 - 2

I DON'T HAVE THE HEART

Words and Music by
JUD FRIEDMAN and
ALLAN RICH

Moderate rock ♩ = 96

TO ME

Words and Music by
MACK DAVID and
MIKE REID

Slowly, with feeling

From the Paramount Motion Picture "DAYS OF THUNDER"

YOU GOTTA LOVE SOMEONE

By
ELTON JOHN/TAUPIN

F3188ASX

From The Broadway Musical "ANNIE"
TOMORROW

Music by
CHARLES STROUSE

Lyric by
MARTIN CHARNIN

TONIGHT I CELEBRATE MY LOVE

Words and Music by
MICHAEL MASSER and
GERRY GOFFIN

TRAVELIN' MAN

**Words and Music by
JERRY FULLER**

THIS OLD HEART OF MINE

(Is Weak For You)

Words and Music by
BRIAN HOLLAND, LAMONT DOZIER,
EDDIE HOLLAND and SYLVIA MOY

Moderate rock ♩ = 116

Paramount Pictures Presents A Lorimar-Martin Elfand Production - A Taylor Hackford Film
"AN OFFICER AND A GENTLEMAN"

UP WHERE WE BELONG

Words by WILL JENNINGS
Music by BUFFY SAINT-MARIE
and JACK NITZSCHE

From The Original Motion Picture Soundtrack "YENTL"

THE WAY HE MAKES ME FEEL

Lyrics by
ALAN and MARILYN BERGMAN

Music by
MICHEL LEGRAND

Slowly and expressively

WE'VE ONLY JUST BEGUN

Lyric by PAUL WILLIAMS
Music by ROGER NICHOLS

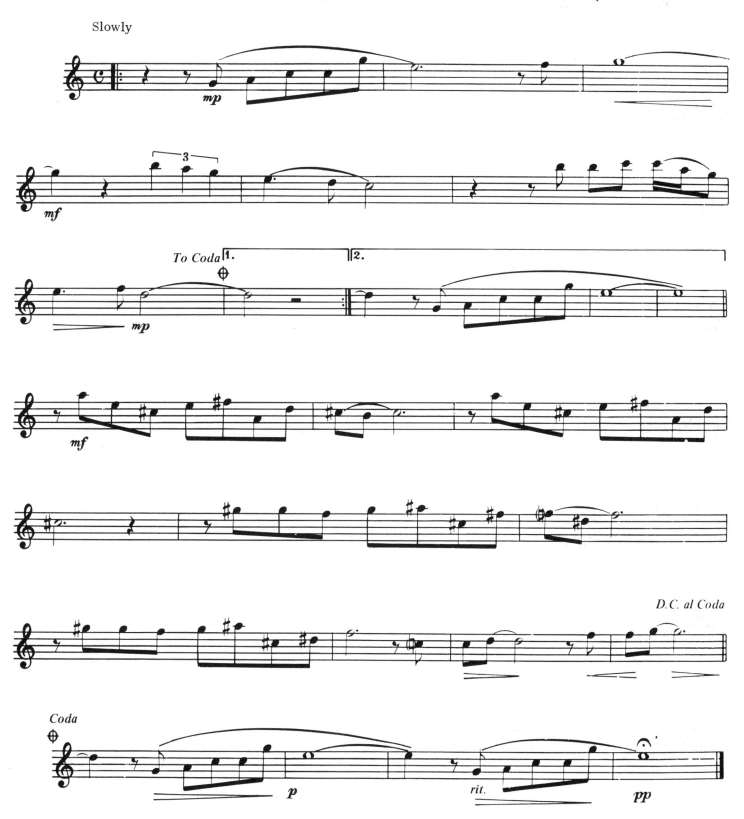

WHAT'S GOING ON

Words and Music by
ALFRED CLEVELAND, MARVIN GAYE
and RENALDO BENSON

WHAT'S LOVE GOT TO DO WITH IT

Words and Music by
GRAHAM LYLE and
TERRY BRITTEN

A WHITE SPORT COAT
(And A Pink Carnation)

Words and Music by
MARTY ROBBINS

YOU ARE THE SUNSHINE OF MY LIFE

By
STEVIE WONDER

YOU AND I

By FRANK MYERS

Moderately Slow

You And I - 2 - 1

D.S. 𝄋

rit.

You And I - 2 - 2

YOU GOT IT ALL

Words and Music by
RUPERT HOLMES

From the Columbia Pictures Release "YOU LIGHT UP MY LIFE"

YOU LIGHT UP MY LIFE

By
JOE BROOKS

YOU'RE THE INSPIRATION

Words and Music by
PETER CETERA and
DAVID FOSTER

OLD TIME ROCK & ROLL

Words and Music by
GEORGE JACKSON and
THOMAS E. JONES III

INSTRUMENTAL
showstoppers

CPP/BELWIN gives you more in this best-selling series! Classics from the '50s right up to the hottest hits of the '90s, plus TV and movie themes. 100 of your favorites including:

- ANYTHING FOR YOU
- DO YOU LOVE ME
- FAME
- FOREVER'S AS FAR AS I'LL GO
- FROM A DISTANCE
- (Everything I Do) I DO IT FOR YOU
- ('Til) I KISSED YOU
- LIGHT MY FIRE
- LINUS AND LUCY
- LOVE THEME FROM ST. ELMO'S FIRE
- MORE THAN WORDS
- OH, PRETTY WOMAN
- OLD TIME ROCK AND ROLL
- PUT A LITTLE LOVE IN YOUR HEART
- WALKING IN MEMPHIS
- WE'VE ONLY JUST BEGUN

Now available for these instruments:

Flute (F2947FLB)
Clarinet (F2947CLC)
Alto Saxophone (F2947ASB)
Tenor Saxophone (F2947TSB)
Trumpet (F2947TRB)
Trombone (F2947TBB)

This music is available at leading music dealers in the United States and Canada.